First published in 2009
by Evans Brothers Limited
2A Portman Mansions
Chiltern Street
London W1U 6NR
UK

Printed in Dubai

British Library Cataloguing in Publication Data
Phillips, Dee.
      Scout. -- (Right now)
      1. Graphic novels. 2. Young adult fiction.
      I. Title II. Series
      741.5-dc22
      ISBN-13: 9780237539542

Developed & Created by R∪bᴊ T∪ᴇsdᴀᴊ Bᴏᴏᴋs Ltd

Project Director – Ruth Owen
Head of Design – Elaine Wilkinson
Designer – Elaine Wilkinson
Editor – Frances Ridley
Consultant – Lorraine Petersen, Chief Executive of NASEN

ACKNOWLEDGEMENTS

With thanks to Lorraine Petersen, Chief Executive of NASEN
for her help in the development and creation of these books.

Images courtesy of Shutterstock

While every effort has been made to secure permission to use copyright material, the publishers
apologise for any errors or omissions in the above list and would be grateful for notification of
any corrections to be included in subsequent editions.

The lights are hot and bright.
The guys are behind me.
This is it!
Tonight is our big chance!

THE ANGEL SHARKS

ONE MOMENT CAN CHANGE YOUR LIFE FOREVER

4

The lights are hot and bright.
They are so bright, I can hardly see.
The guys are behind me.
This is it!
Tonight is our big chance!

I look out over the crowd.
I'm looking for the girl.
The girl with the bright
red hair.

The girl who is a scout for
a major record company.

She has to be here.

6

I turn to the guys.

ONE,
TWO,
THREE...

8

I start to sing.
We sound great.
It's my favourite song.
The song that got all this started.

9

At the start it was just Alex and me.
Alex was the new kid in our year.
One day, we got talking.
Talking about music.

Alex

Pete

Alex and I liked the same music.
We liked R&B.
We liked old American stuff.
Alex liked The Doors.
I liked Pink Floyd.
We had our own ideas, too.

One day, I showed Alex
one of my songs.
I sang him a couple of lines.

Alex picked up his guitar.

He played a few chords.

The music sounded great.

13

By the end of the day we had our first song.
That was the best day of my life.
I wanted to do this forever.
I wanted to sing and make records.

I turn to look at Alex.
He is playing his guitar.
His eyes are closed.
This is our favourite song.
It's about our music hero.
It's the song we wrote
together, that day.

17

The crowd cheers and claps.
I start to sing the next song.
It's a sad, slow song.
I wrote this song when my
girlfriend Jo dumped me!

Then suddenly I see the girl.
The girl with the bright red hair.
This is it!
This is our big chance!

Alex and I practised every day after school.
I wrote more songs.

Then one day, Alex said, "We sound great, but we could be even better." He said, "We need more people, Pete."

So we put an ad in the newspaper.

It was like *The X Factor*.
Old people came along.
Young kids.
Punks. Goths. Rappers.
A thrash metal band.

Sam   Nat   Nick

But that's how we found Sam, Nat and Nick.
Now we were a real band.

The band needed a name.
We tried movie names and words.
We tried just opening a dictionary.

James Bond

Angel

Heat wave

Jaws

Rocks

Iron Man

Retro

Target

That's how we became

THE ANGEL SHARKS.

I wrote the songs and did the singing.
Alex was our leader.

Nat was the joker.
Sometimes we argued, but
Nat would make us laugh.

Alex got us our first gig.
We played at his sister's birthday party.

We practised every weekend.
It was great.
I wanted to do this forever.

Sam got us online.

THE ANGEL SHARKS

We made CDs of our songs.
We sent them to record companies.
We were a great team.

That was three years ago.
Three years of gigs.
Three years of sending out CDs.

Then yesterday the girl called me.
She said she was a music scout.
A scout from a major record company.
She had our CD.
She wanted to come to our gig.

She said, "My name is Carly. Look out for me. I have bright red hair."

The gig is over.
Tonight, we sounded great.
I look out over the crowd.
Carly the scout is waiting for us.

Alex says, "Go on Pete. Talk to her. This is it!"

I walk over to Carly.
She says, "You were great.
I love your songs."
She says, "I want to record you."
I say, "I'll get the other guys."

But Carly shakes her head.
She says, "I want to record
you, Pete

She says, is OK,
but

39

I turn to look at the guys.
They are having fun.
They are nervous and excited.

MUSIC HEROES
ON YOUR OWN

Alex and Pete talk about their music heroes.

- Who are your music heroes?
- Why are they your heroes?
- What style of music do they play?
- What are the best songs they have sung?
- Write a playlist of your favourite tracks.
- List three reasons why people should listen to them.

JAMMING
WITH A PARTNER

"Jamming" means trying out different ideas for songs. Have a go at jamming with a friend!

- Start with a beat. Use drums, or just clap.
- Add some words. They could be about school, friendship… or love!
- Mess around with your words until you are happy. Use them to make a song or a rap.

Alex

TEAMWORK
IN A GROUP

Pete

The band members all work together as a team. How will they react to Carly's plan for Pete?

Sam

- Look through the book. Make notes on the personalities of the band members.

- Choose which band member you want to role-play. How will your character react to the news? What will your character say to the others?

Nick

- Role-play the band's discussion after the gig. What does everyone think Pete should do?

Nat

BAND WiTHOUT A NAME
ON YOUR OWN / WITH A PARTNER / IN A GROUP

A band's name gives you clues about their sound and their look. It might even tell you what they believe in.

- Think of famous band names. Why do you think the bands chose those names?

- Think of a name for a new band. What places could you look for ideas? Try TV shows, movies, online, look in the dictionary, look for words around you!

It's just an old, empty house.
Lauren must spend the night
inside. Just Lauren and the ghost...

Tonight, Vicky must make a
choice. Stay in London with
her boyfriend Chris. Or start
a new life in Australia.

Dan sees the red car.
The keys are inside. Dan
says to Andy, Sam and Jess,
"Want to go for a drive?"